THE GOLDEN COMPASS

LEVEL 2

SCHOLASTIC

Adapted by: Jane Rollason
Publisher: Jacquie Bloese
Editor: Patricia Reilly
Designer: Eddie Rego
Picture research: Emma Bree
Photo credits:
Cover and inside images courtesy of
New Line Productions, Inc.
Page 48: D. Levenson/Getty Images.
Page 49: E. Bree/Mary Glasgow Magazines.

Adapted from *The Golden Compass*™ movie
screenplay by Paul Harrison

Published by Scholastic Ltd. 2008

Mary Glasgow Magazines (Scholastic Ltd.)
Euston House
24 Eversholt Street
London NW1 IDB

Printed in Singapore. Reprinted in 2010.

Contents

	Page

The Golden Compass

People and dœmons	4-5
People and places	6-7
Prologue: The world of the Golden Compass	8
Chapter 1: Oxford	9
Chapter 2: Mrs Coulter	14
Chapter 3: London	17
Chapter 4: To the North	22
Chapter 5: Trollesund	27
Chapter 6: The Experimental Station	31
Chapter 7: A dangerous machine	35
Chapter 8: The land of the Ice Bears	40
Chapter 9: Another world	44
Fact Files	48-53
The writer	48
Lyra's world	50
Find your dœmon	52
Self-Study Activities	54-56
New Words	inside back cover

THE WORLD OF THE GOLDEN COMPASS

Lyra Belacqua is twelve. She lives at Jordan College in Oxford. She's clever and loves adventure.

Dæmon: Pantalaimon, or Pan for short. Pan is always changing his form.

Lord Asriel is Lyra's uncle. He travels to new places and finds out about them. He sometimes visits Lyra at Jordan College. He has just come back from travelling in the Arctic.

Dæmon: Stelmaria, a big snow cat.

Mrs Coulter is an important person in the Magisterium and lives in London. She's beautiful and knows what she wants. She is very interested in Lyra - but is she dangerous?

Dæmon: the Golden Monkey. He never speaks and he has no name.

Roger Parslow is Lyra's best friend in Oxford. He's twelve and he works in the Jordan College kitchens. He and Lyra love playing games.

Dæmon: Salcilia.

Lee Scoresby is a friend of Iorek's. He comes from Texas and he flies his own airship. He always says what he thinks.

Dæmon: Hester.

Iorek Byrnison is an armoured Ice Bear or Panserbjørne. He is living in Trollesund in Norroway. Some people from the Magisterium took away his armour.

Ice Bears don't have dæmons.

What is a 'dæmon'*?

In the world of the Golden Compass, each person has a dæmon. Your dæmon is part of you, but it lives outside your body. It takes the form of an animal. It thinks and feels the same things as you. Energy lines join a person and his or her dæmon together. They have to stay close together.

A girl's dæmon is usually a boy. A boy's dæmon is usually a girl. A child's dæmon can change its form. But when the child grows up, the dæmon chooses one form forever.

* You pronounce the word 'dæmon' like the English word 'demon'.

 # PEOPLE AND PLACES

PEOPLE

The **Master** is the head of Jordan College. The **Jordan Scholars** are the teachers.

Fra Pavel works for the Magisterium. He is a dangerous man.

The **Witches of Lake Enara** live for hundreds of years. They are strong fighters and they can fly. Their queen is Serafina Pekkala.

The **Gyptians** live on riverboats and ships; they buy and sell things around the world. Their king is John Faa. They are always ready to fight.

The **Panserbjørne** are armoured Ice Bears. They make and wear their own armour. They can talk and they are intelligent. They live in Svalbard in the far north. Their king is Ragnar Sturlusson.

The **Tartars** and the Samoyeds live near Bolvangar in Norroway. The Tartars are famous fighters, and their wolf-dæmons are very frightening.

PLACES

Oxford and **London** in Brytain and **Trollesund** in Norroway look like places in our world – but they are very different. There are no cars, and people sometimes travel by sky ferry. **Bolvangar** is also in Norroway. **Svalbard** is a small land in the far north.

The **Experimental Station** is near Bolvangar. The Tartars don't allow anyone to get close to it. What is happening there?

The **Magisterium** controls Lyra's world. Fra Pavel and Mrs Coulter work for the Magisterium. The Magisterium doesn't like Lord Asriel or his work.

Lyra lives at **Jordan College**, in Oxford.

The **Golden Compass** is another name for the **alethiometer**. It is very old. If you know how to read the alethiometer, it answers all your questions. Everybody wants it, but not many people can read it.

THE WORLD OF
THE GOLDEN COMPASS

Our world is one of many worlds. Lyra Belacqua lives in the world of the Golden Compass. Her world is like our world in some ways, but it's also very different. She is twelve years old and has no parents. She lives at Jordan College in Oxford.

The Jordan scholars look after her. Her uncle, Lord Asriel, sent her there when she was very young.

Lyra does not know, but her world is about to change for ever. There is a very old prophecy. It says that Lyra will decide the future of her world, and of all the worlds everywhere …

CHAPTER 1
Oxford

Lyra walked quietly through the dusty rooms of Jordan College. She came to the Dining Room. The table was ready for the Jordan Scholars. At the other end of the Dining Room was the Scholars' special room, called the Retiring Room. The Scholars didn't allow Lyra to go in there, so of course she wanted to see it. Her dæmon Pantalaimon – or Pan for short – ran behind her.

'Shh Lyra!' said Pan quietly. 'You're too noisy. They'll catch us!'

'Nobody can hear us,' said Lyra. 'Don't worry!'

Lyra went into the Retiring Room. Pan changed into a bird and flew in behind her. They were looking around when suddenly they heard people outside. They quickly climbed into a cupboard. A man came in with some wine and some glasses and put them on the table.
The Master of Jordan College and Fra Pavel followed him into the room. Fra Pavel was from The Magisterium – the Magisterium controlled Lyra's world. The Master and Pavel were talking about Lord Asriel and his new idea.

'You are Master of Jordan. You must stop him!' shouted Pavel.

The Master did not agree. Asriel was an important man and a good man.

'He is a Jordan Scholar,' said the Master. 'If he wants to go, he can go.'

Fra Pavel was not happy with the Master's answer. He waited for the Master to leave the room. Then he quickly put something into the wine. He smiled a small smile, and then he left too.

'He's trying to kill Uncle Asriel!' said Lyra.

'You don't know that,' said Pan. 'And we're in trouble if someone finds us here.'

At that moment, Lord Asriel came into the room with his dæmon, Stelmaria. He wanted a drink before the others arrived. He put some wine into a glass. He was about to drink it when the cupboard door crashed open. Lyra jumped from the cupboard and hit the glass out of her uncle's hand. It broke. Lord Asriel was very surprised and caught Lyra's arm.

'The man from the Magisterium wants to kill you,' she cried. 'He put something in the wine! I saw him.'

Asriel smelt the wine, but then they heard people outside the room.

'Quick!' he said. He pushed Lyra and Pan back into the cupboard.

The Master and the Scholars came into the room. They sat down and waited for Lord Asriel to start. Pavel looked quickly at the floor and saw the pieces of glass.

Asriel turned on a large machine. A picture appeared in the air in front of them. It was a man and his dæmon. Something around them was glowing.

'I went to the Arctic twelve months ago,' Asriel said.
'I took this picture at the North Pole in Svalbard. Something is coming down from the sky to the man. It isn't light. It's Dust.'

The Scholars all started to talk excitedly.

'What's Dust?' Lyra asked her dæmon quietly. But Pan didn't know.

'As you can see,' said Asriel, 'the Dust is going through the man's dæmon and into him. Where does this Dust come from? I want to find out.'

At the top of the picture there was a shining city. It was hanging in the sky.

'This is a city in another world – a world next to ours – but one of many worlds,' said Asriel. 'Dust comes from there and other worlds. I plan to travel there.'

Fra Pavel did not like this idea at all. But the Scholars were very interested. They agreed to give Asriel money for his work.

After the Scholars left, Asriel pulled Lyra from the cupboard. They walked quickly across the college. Asriel did not answer her questions.

'Can I come with you?' she asked. 'I want to learn about Dust and everything!'

'What do you know about Dust?' Asriel asked angrily.

'Nothing,' answered Lyra.

'Good. Never ask about it again. Be a good girl, and I'll bring you a nice present from the North Pole.'

He didn't say goodbye. He just left.

That night, Lyra met her best friend Roger Parslow high up on top of the college. It was their favourite meeting place. They were talking about the Gobblers. They were frightened of the Gobblers.

'They take children from all around Oxford,' said Roger.

'And then they eat them,' said Lyra. 'Roger, the Gobblers could catch you. But I'll rescue you – you know that, don't you?'

'The Gobblers won't get me!' said Roger.

'You'll rescue me too, won't you?' asked Lyra.

'Of course I will. But your uncle's an important man – everybody will look for you.'

This was true, but Lyra didn't like this idea.

'You're just as important as me, Roger,' she said angrily.

Suddenly someone called from below.

'Lyra! Come and put your best clothes on! The Master wants you.'

After Lyra went, Roger walked alone around the college gardens. He was bored. Then he heard something.

'Lyra? Is that you?' he called. His dæmon Salcilia changed into a bird. She flew around. Suddenly a golden monkey appeared and caught Salcilia in its hand. A dark form moved towards Roger.

'Let me go! Let Salcilia go!' cried Roger. But nobody heard him.

CHAPTER 2
Mrs Coulter

Lyra sat in the Dining Room. Her clothes were uncomfortable, and her face and hands were cleaner than usual. Jordan Scholars sat at tables all around her.

The Master was talking to her.

'Lyra,' he said, 'you must understand – your studies are very important. Sometimes we know better than you.'

'I disagree, Master,' a voice said.

The Master stopped speaking. A tall, beautiful woman stood next to him.

'Who's she?' said Pan in Lyra's ear.

'Dunno,' answered Lyra. 'But the Master's frightened of her!'

'Mrs Coulter,' said the Master. 'This is Lyra. Lyra, this is Mrs Coulter. A … a friend of the college.'

Mrs Coulter sat next to Lyra. While they ate, she told Lyra stories of the Ice Bears in Svalbard – the Panserbjørne.

'The King of the Ice Bears is called Ragnar Sturlusson. He only wants one thing – his own dæmon. Bears don't have dæmons, you see.'

Lyra really liked the beautiful stranger. And then Mrs Coulter had a wonderful idea.

'I'm going back to the North very soon,' she said. 'I will need a helper. Why don't you come?'

Lyra was very excited by the idea, but the Master was worried.

'Lord Asriel wants Lyra to study at Jordan College with us,' he said.

'Let me talk to Lord Asriel,' said Mrs Coulter.

The Master agreed unhappily. Lyra was very happy, she wanted to spend more time with Mrs Coulter. But Pan did not like Mrs Coulter's dæmon – the Golden Monkey.

The next day, the Master visited Lyra in her room. He looked very worried, and he carried a little bag.

'I must speak to you,' he said to Lyra. He took something from the bag. It was small, round and golden. It was like a compass.

'This is an alethiometer,' he said, and gave it to her. 'It was Lord Asriel's. Now I am giving it to you. I think you are meant to have it.'

'What does it do?' asked Lyra.

'It gives true answers to your questions,' answered the Master.

'How does it work?'

'Long ago people knew the answer to that, but now nobody knows. I must ask you to remember one very important thing – you must never show it to Mrs Coulter. You must never tell her that you have it.'

Lyra was surprised by the Master's words. She was worried, too. But she left with Mrs Coulter anyway.

When Lyra walked out of Jordan College, the Master and another Scholar watched from the Retiring Room.

'We cannot help her now,' said the Master sadly.

'We have done our best,' said the Scholar.

'Yes, but you know what the prophecy says,' answered the Master.

'You don't believe that old story, do you?' asked the Scholar.

At that moment the door crashed open. Fra Pavel quickly came in with some Magisterial men.

'Master, you must come with us,' shouted Pavel. He was very angry. 'You are going to prison. You helped Lord Asriel, but the Magisterium does not like his work. Now, tell me. Where is the alethiometer?'

The Master just smiled.

CHAPTER 3
London

Outside the college Lyra and Mrs Coulter were about to get on the sky ferry* to London.

'Where's Roger?' Lyra asked.

'Who's Roger?' answered Mrs Coulter.

Lyra explained, but Mrs Coulter didn't want to wait.

'Hurry up!' she said and walked quickly on to the sky ferry with Lyra.

The sky ferry was a very comfortable way to travel. Lyra and Pan looked down at the city of London below. They could see the London Magisterium building, and lots of other tall buildings.

'Isn't it fantastic?' said Lyra to Pan.

* A sky ferry is a way of travelling by air in Lyra's world.

After Oxford, London seemed very noisy and strange to Lyra. There were sky ferries above their heads, tall buildings around them and a lot of people on the streets. She liked Mrs Coulter's home. Everything looked very expensive, but it was very comfortable too.

Lyra's first few days in London were very busy. Mrs Coulter bought her fine new clothes and took her to dinner parties. Lyra felt very important. Nobody wanted to talk to her in Oxford. But here, everyone wanted to talk to her. Pan didn't like it at all.

'Mrs Coulter wants to show everyone her new pet – you!' he said unkindly.

'You just don't like her,' answered Lyra. 'Well, bad luck, because I like her.'

But Lyra did feel a little uncomfortable. She did not tell Mrs Coulter about the alethiometer. She remembered the Master's words, and didn't say anything. She always carried it with her in the little bag. At night, she slept with it in her bed.

Soon, Lyra discovered that something was not quite right. Mrs Coulter and Lyra were at home one night after a dinner party. They were talking about one of the other guests.

'He is a clever man,' said Mrs Coulter. 'He studies particle metaphysics*. Have I told you about particles?'

'You mean Dust?' said Lyra. She felt very clever.

Suddenly Mrs Coulter wasn't smiling.

'What do you know about Dust?' she asked coldly.

'That … that … it comes from the sky,' said Lyra.

'There are some things we don't speak about,' answered Mrs Coulter.

'But I didn't …' Lyra started to say.

'Yes, yes, I know. You didn't know. Well, don't do it again. Now, can you please take off that stupid bag? I hate to see it. You always wear it in the house.'

Lyra held the bag close.

'I won't take it off,' she said.

'Do what I tell you! I will always win when we don't agree,' said Mrs Coulter. 'Remember that!'

Suddenly, the Golden Monkey caught Pan and pulled him further and further away from Lyra. The energy lines

* Particle metaphysics is the study of the smallest pieces of life and the world.

which joined Pan and Lyra pulled hard. They both felt terrible. Lyra had no choice – she had to put the bag down.

Mrs Coulter looked at Lyra. 'I win,' she said, and she and her dæmon left the room.

Lyra and Pan were very angry with Mrs Coulter and the Golden Monkey.

'I hate them both!' said Lyra. 'Why do they want us here?'

That night, they went downstairs very quietly. They went into Mrs Coulter's study and looked at her papers. Pan found pages with children's names on them. Next to each child's name the words 'Dust Count' appeared, followed by the word 'Intercision'.

'What's "intercision"?' asked Pan.

'I dunno,' said Lyra.

'And look at the name at the top of the pages,' said Pan.

'The General Oblation Board – the G.O.B.-'

'Gobblers!' cried Lyra. 'And look! Mrs Coulter has signed the bottom of each page. She's the head of the Gobblers!'

At that moment they heard Mrs Coulter's voice. She was calling Lyra. Quickly, Lyra and Pan ran out of the room. Then, they walked more slowly away from the study. Mrs Coulter appeared in front of them.

'Lyra,' said Mrs Coulter sweetly. 'What are you doing?'

'Nothing,' answered Lyra.

'Then come and help me,' said Mrs Coulter. But then Lyra heard a sound. It was coming from her bedroom.

Lyra ran to her room. The Golden Monkey was there, and it was holding the alethiometer. Pan changed into a bird. He took the alethiometer from the monkey's hand and flew through the window. Lyra quickly climbed out of the window and followed him into the night.

CHAPTER 4
To the North

Lyra and Pan walked through the dark streets of London – but they were not alone. Three men were following them. Lyra and Pan ran, but they didn't run fast enough. The men caught them.

Suddenly, some other people appeared – some Gyptians! Gyptians were travellers and fighters. They were stronger than the three men, and they rescued Lyra and Pan. Lyra knew Ma Costa, one of the Gyptian rescuers. She was the mother of Billy Costa – a friend of Lyra's in Oxford.

'We saw you leave Jordan College and followed you to London,' Ma Costa explained to Lyra. 'We've watched over you since then. Now we're going to meet the King of the Gyptians, John Faa. He's called us all together – all the Gyptians. We're going north. The Gobblers have taken lots of children to the North. We're going to rescue them. Come with us.'

Lyra joined the Gyptians. They went down the River Thames on Ma Costa's riverboat.

But on the other side of London, Mrs Coulter was still looking for Lyra.

'She's probably with the Gyptians,' she thought. She had some Gyptian spies in prison. The Magisterial men caught the Gyptians when they were spying on the Magisterium. She decided to let one of the spies escape, then she sent two Spy-flies* after him. The Spy-flies flew fast into the sky.

Ma Costa's riverboat arrived at John Faa's ship, the Noorderlicht, in the North Sea. Lyra met the King of the Gyptians and Farder Coram. He was an old and very

* Spy-flies are small machines which look like a fly. The Magisterium uses them for spying.

clever Gyptian. Lyra showed them the alethiometer.

Farder Coram studied it very closely. It was like a compass with pictures around the edge. It had three hands, like a clock, and one fine long hand. When someone asked it a question, they moved the three hands to point to different pictures. These pictures showed their question. Then the thin hand pointed to more pictures. This was the alethiometer's answer.

'I have a question for it,' said John Faa. 'Where are my Gyptian spies?'

But Farder Coram could not read the pictures.

'Please can I try?' asked Lyra. She took the alethiometer and moved the hands. Nothing happened at first, but then the alethiometer answered. 'It says they're dead,' said Lyra.

'I hope you have read it wrongly, child,' said John Faa.

'Where's Billy Costa?' she asked. 'I haven't seen him.'

'The Gobblers have got him,' said John Faa. 'And Roger Parslow, too. They're taking them to the North.'

At that moment, a Gyptian fell onto the ship. It was Jacob Huismans, one of John Faa's spies. He was dying.

'Where are the other spies?' John Faa asked Jacob.

'Some are dead … Mrs Coulter has the others in prison.'

'So, you read the alethiometer right, Lyra,' said Farder Coram.

And then the Spy-flies arrived! They flew at the Gyptians fast and attacked them angrily. But the Gyptians and their dæmons, and Pan were too quick for them. One Spy-fly escaped, but they caught the other one in a box. They gave it to Lyra.

John Faa's ship started for the North. That night, Lyra and Pan stood outside on the ship and watched the black waters. Suddenly, a dark form appeared from the sky. It flew silently down next to Lyra. It was a beautiful young woman. The woman spoke, but not out loud. Lyra heard the words in her head.

'I am Serafina Pekkala, Queen of the Witches of Lake Enara,' she said. 'Give Farder Coram a message from me. I know the place that he is looking for, it is called Bolvangar. It is a terrible place. The Tartars and their dæmons attack anybody who tries to go near it. It takes a week to get there on foot from Trollesund in Norroway.'

And the beautiful Serafina Pekkala flew quietly away into the dark night.

CHAPTER 5
Trollesund

Lyra gave Serafina's message to Farder Coram and then the Noorderlicht slowly travelled to Trollesund. When the ship arrived, Lyra found a quiet place to sit. She wanted to practise reading the alethiometer. Other people could not understand its answers, but she seemed to understand them easily.

'That's a very fine-looking piece,' said a deep voice.

Lyra looked up. A tall man was standing in front of her. He had long white hair and a friendly face.

'My name's Lee Scoresby,' he said. 'And this old girl is Hester,' he said, pointing to his dæmon.

'I'm Lyra and this is Pan,' she answered, 'Pleased to meet you.'

'I usually work in my airship,' said Lee Scoresby. 'But I'm here to help a friend who's in trouble.'

'Me too,' said Lyra. 'The Gobblers have taken my friend Roger. I'm going to rescue him.'

'Well, Lyra,' said Lee, 'rescuing your friend will be a difficult job. I think you need a man with an airship and you need an armoured bear. There's a bear in town. His name's Iorek Byrnison. He works here.'

He touched his hat to say goodbye and left.

That night Lyra and Farder Coram went to look for the armoured bear. They came to a place which was full of old broken boats and bits of wood. And there was the bear – a great big bear – sitting down. He wasn't wearing armour, but he still looked dangerous. He was eating a piece of meat and there was blood on his white coat.

'Iorek Byrnison,' said Farder Coram, 'I offer you work.'

'I have work,' answered the bear.

'What kind of work is this for a Panserbjørne?' Coram asked.

'Paid work,' said Iorek, and he reached for a bottle of whisky.

'Is that how they pay you?' asked Lyra. 'With whisky?'

Farder Coram turned to leave. He was about to walk

away, when Lyra spoke again.

'Iorek Byrnison! I have heard that bears live to catch their food and to fight. They fight well and they are never frightened. Why are you here? You are better than this!'

Iorek's strong body moved angrily.

'When I came here, they gave me whisky. I fell asleep. While I slept, they took my armour. Without my armour … I am nothing. I am nothing anyway. I had to leave the land of the Ice Bears because I lost a fight with another bear.'

Iorek turned away. He felt sorry for himself. Farder Coram again turned to leave, but Lyra quickly asked the alethiometer a question. Then she ran to the Ice Bear.

'Your armour is in the Magisterium office,' she said.

Iorek was very surprised and pleased. He stood up on his great legs.

'I will work for you until I die or until you win,' he said.

Without another word, Iorek ran off to get his armour.

Lyra ran after Iorek. There was a lot of shouting and crashing in the centre of Trollesund.

'A great white bear has pulled the doors off the Magisterium building,' someone said.

The Magisterial police were outside the building. With a
great roar, Iorek crashed through the wall. He was wearing
his armour and he was ready to fight. Lyra ran to him.

'Please don't fight here, Iorek,' she called. 'Please!
We must rescue Roger and the other children.'

The police pointed their guns at Iorek.

Just then, Lee Scoresby and the Gyptians arrived.
They pointed their guns at the police. Now there were
more Gyptians than police.

'Hold it!' shouted Scoresby. Then he looked at the bear.
'Hello, Iorek,' he said. 'I couldn't think how to help you
escape. Luckily, this little girl is really clever.'

He turned to the police.

'Why don't you go?' he said.

The men from the Magisterium started to move away.

CHAPTER 6
The Experimental Station

Now Iorek and Lee Scoresby were working with the Gyptians. They all left Trollesund on foot, but Lee Scoresby took his airship with him. They walked north all day. When night fell, they stopped to eat and sleep. Lyra found Iorek and spoke to him alone.

'The alethiometer tells me there is a small building over the next hill. It's on a small piece of land in the middle of some water. It has something to do with the Gobblers. Could you take me there?'

Iorek was surprised, but he agreed to help.

With Lyra on his back, Iorek quickly reached the little building. It was a terrible, lost place.

'Something feels very wrong here,' said Iorek.

Pan felt uncomfortable too. Lyra and Pan went into the little building. Inside there was a boy – he was very unhappy and alone … completely alone.

'Where's his dæmon?' asked Pan. He felt terrible.

Suddenly Lyra understood.

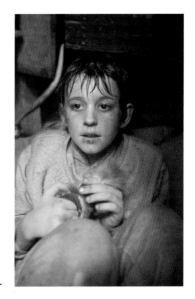

'That's it!' she cried. 'That's "intercision". Remember on the papers in Mrs Coulter's room? Next to each child's name, it said "Dust Count" and "Intercision". That's it! That's what the Gobblers are doing. They're cutting off the kids' dæmons!'

Lyra slowly helped the boy to stand up and they went outside. Suddenly, she saw that the boy was her friend, Billy Costa. Iorek quickly carried Lyra and Billy back to the Gyptians. It wasn't a happy moment for Ma Costa. Her son had no dæmon – he seemed to be less than half a child. He didn't even know who she was.

But there was no time to think. Suddenly, the Gyptians were under attack.

'Samoyeds!' someone shouted.

At once, Samoyeds and Gyptians were shouting and fighting. The Samoyeds caught Lyra, but nobody saw. They took her away with them.

They travelled fast all through the night. Finally, they reached a group of buildings. A man took Lyra into a big light room. It was soon clear that the people there didn't know who she was. She was just another child to them.

'What is this place?' she asked one of the men.

'You'll like it,' he answered. 'It's called the "Experimental Station". It was lucky that the Samoyeds found you and brought you here. You were lost in the snow.'

'I wasn't lost, there was fighting,' said Lyra. 'The Samoyeds attacked us and caught me.'

'Oh, I don't think so,' said the man. 'Often, in the cold, you fall asleep and have bad dreams. When you wake up, you can't remember what's true and what isn't true.'

'What do you do here?' asked Lyra.

'We help children grow up,' he said with a smile.

Then a worker in white clothes took Lyra to a very big dining room.

Lyra walked into the dining room – and there was Roger!

Lyra didn't want anybody to know that she knew Roger. She smiled at him, but she didn't say anything. There was a space next to him and she sat down.

'I knew it! I knew it!' said Roger quietly, but very excitedly. He was very pleased to see her.

'I've come to rescue you with the Gyptians, Roger. But I need to go somewhere quiet. I want to find out when the Gyptians are coming.'

CHAPTER 7
A dangerous machine

Lyra and Roger left the big dining room. Lyra went into a small dining room while Roger waited outside. She took out the alethiometer.

'That's strange,' Lyra said to Pan. 'The only thing the alethiometer says is, "Don't let Mrs Coulter get the alethiometer or we'll all die."'

At that moment, Lyra heard a loud voice outside. She went as cold as ice. It was Mrs Coulter!

'How did those children get out of the station?' she was asking. She had two Bolvangar workers in white coats with her. Roger wasn't there – he disappeared as soon as he heard voices. Lyra hid under the dining-room table just before Mrs Coulter and her men came in.

'Anyway,' said Mrs Coulter, 'I have some good news. Lord Asriel is in trouble with Fra Pavel and the Magisterium. They have sent him to Svalbard. The king of the bears is keeping him there.'

Lyra looked at Pan. This was terrible news – Lord Asriel was a prisoner!

'I'm tired,' said Mrs Coulter, 'I have travelled a long way today, I'm going to bed.' She left the room.

When Mrs Coulter left, Lyra felt better. She moved a little and by accident she hit the table leg. Mrs Coulter's men heard her and found her at once. They took her out of the small dining room, and into a big white room with a large machine in it. It was like a hospital. The men put Lyra and Pan into different parts of the machine.

Lyra was shouting and fighting.

'Be quiet!' said one of the men. 'You want to grow up, don't you?'

'It's only a little cut,' said another.

A doctor turned the machine on. The machine started to glow. Lyra could see lines of energy that joined her and Pan. The machine was going to cut the energy lines!

'What is going on in here?' a voice suddenly said. It was Mrs Coulter. Everyone became silent. 'And who is this child …Lyra!'

Lyra's eyes closed.

Lyra woke up suddenly and felt very frightened. Was it all a dream? Pan was still there … but Mrs Coulter was there too.

'You're going to be fine, Lyra,' said Mrs Coulter in a soft voice.

'But Roger … and the other kids … why are you cutting off their dæmons? It's so horrible.'

'It seems horrible,' said Mrs Coulter, 'but it's good for them. It's just a little cut and then they'll always be safe from Dust.'

'I don't understand,' said Lyra. 'Why is Dust so bad?'

'Dust is very very bad,' said Mrs Coulter. 'A long time ago, someone did something very bad. They didn't do what the Authority told them. Because of that, Dust came into the world. We've all been ill since then.'

Mrs Coulter put her arms around Lyra.

'Children, you see, don't have Dust. The Dust comes later on, when you grow up and your dæmon stops changing. The Dust gives you bad ideas and feelings, but one little cut stops this. And your dæmon doesn't die, it just becomes your special pet.'

Lyra looked at Mrs Coulter. 'Is this true?' she thought.

'There's something else, Lyra. Your mother didn't die. You see, she wasn't married to your father. She loved you very much, but she wasn't allowed to keep you. She wanted you back. Later, when she was a stronger person, your mother went to Jordan College …'

'No!' shouted Lyra.

'Yes, Lyra. I am your mother.'

'Then who is my father?' asked Lyra. But suddenly she knew the answer. It was Lord Asriel!

'And now, please give me the alethiometer,' said Mrs Coulter.

Lyra took a box from her bag and gave it to Mrs Coulter. It was the box with the Spy-fly. Mrs Coulter opened it – the Spy-fly flew out and attacked the Golden Monkey.

'Run, Pan!' shouted Lyra. Lyra and Pan ran as fast as they could. Lyra stopped for a moment.

'We need to wake the children up,' she said to Pan.

Pan pointed to a glass box on the wall. It said, 'Break if there is a fire'. Lyra broke the glass and at once a loud sound filled the building. As Lyra hoped, the children came out of the long bedrooms to see what was happening. They were still half-asleep.

'Come on!' shouted Lyra.

The children ran through the big white room, but Lyra stopped and looked at the cutting machine. There was a heavy box on a desk. She threw it at the machine. With a loud crash, the terrible machine broke into a thousand pieces. Lyra ran after the other children.

The children ran out into the cold night. Behind them, the Bolvangar workers were shouting, but they didn't stop. When they were outside, the children heard a really frightening sound and stopped running. It was the Tartars and their dæmons. They stood in a line in front of the children. The children couldn't move past them.

'Go on then!' Lyra shouted to the Tartars.

A dæmon ran to attack her. It jumped, but then a great white arm pushed it away. It was Iorek! He roared and ran at the Tartars. The Tartars got ready to fire their guns, but the order to fire never came. From above, the witches flew down and attacked the Tartars. From the sides, John Faa and the Gyptians fired at them. The Gyptians quickly rescued all the children.

A Tartar ran at Lyra and Roger, but someone stopped him from above. They looked up. It was Lee Scoresby in his airship. He held a gun in his hand!

'Lyra!' he called. 'You wanted to try flying, didn't you?'

Lyra wanted to reach Svalbard and rescue Lord Asriel, so she climbed into the airship with Iorek and Roger. Lee turned the airship to the north, and they went towards the land of the Ice Bears. Serafina flew with them.

CHAPTER 8
The land of the Ice Bears

As the airship came closer to Svalbard, Lee Scoresby sat and talked to Serafina. She was sitting on the edge of the airship, while Lyra, Roger and Iorek slept inside.
The Witch Queen told Lee about a prophecy.

'It says that a war is coming,' she told Lee. 'And Lyra will decide who wins the war.'

'What will this war be about?' asked Lee.

'The Magisterium wants to control this world and every other world. They cannot control other worlds yet.
Lord Asriel is finding a way to travel between worlds. Perhaps they will find it too. Then nothing will stop them. Nothing but us … and that child.'

Suddenly the airship flew into a snowstorm. Everyone woke up. A strong wind pushed the ship onto its side, and Lyra started to fall out. She reached for Lee Scoresby's hand, but he couldn't catch her. She fell over the edge. Luckily, the ship wasn't too high and Lyra and Pan fell onto soft snow. They looked at the white world around them. They had no idea where they were.

Then two great white bears appeared out of the snow – Panserbjørne!

'You are our prisoner. Come with us,' roared one of the bears. The bears took Lyra and Pan to the palace of the bear king, Ragnar Sturlusson.

'Don't worry,' said Pan to Lyra, 'Iorek will come.'

'But they'll kill him before he gets close,' said Lyra sadly.

Armoured bears stood all around Ragnar's ice palace. The two bears took their prisoners into a great room. There was blood on the walls and dead fish on the floor.

It smelt terrible. And there was the king of the
Ice Bears.

Ragnar was even bigger than Iorek. He had a big strong
body. He looked at Lyra through half-closed eyes.
He didn't see Pan.

Suddenly she remembered Mrs Coulter's words:
"Ragnar wants only one thing – his own dæmon. Bears
don't have dæmons, you see." This gave Lyra an idea.

'Quick, Pan,' she said. 'Hide inside my
coat. I don't want Ragnar to know I've
got a dæmon!'

Then she spoke to the king.
'Good day, great king!'
cried Lyra.

'And who are you?' asked the
king angrily.

'I am Iorek Byrnison's
dæmon,' answered Lyra.
Ragnar was very surprised and
very angry.

'But,' said Lyra, 'I want to be your dæmon. You are better in every way. Iorek has left the land of the Ice Bears, but he is coming here to fight you. I am sure you will win and then I will be your dæmon. But you must kill him – one against one in a fair fight.'

Ragnar was quiet for a moment.

'I won last time I fought Iorek,' thought Ragnar, 'I can win again. This time, I will finish him.'

'Yes!' he cried. And then he did something very strange for a bear – he smiled.

Iorek soon appeared, with Roger on his back.

Lyra was worried. 'Have I done the wrong thing?' she thought.

She told Iorek about her plan.

'The fight with Ragnar has already saved you,' she said. 'Ragnar told his bears not to kill you. He wants to fight you.'

Iorek was pleased.

'You are a very clever girl,' he said. 'And I really want to fight him.'

Ragnar waited at the fighting place – it was a square outside the palace doors. Panserbjørne stood around the edges. Ragnar and Iorek roared loudly and the fight started. It was hard and terrible. Soon, there was blood all over the snow. Both bears hit as hard as they could. Ragnar seemed to be winning. He cut Iorek's left arm badly. Iorek tried to hit back with his right arm, but he wasn't strong enough. Ragnar attacked Iorek again and again.

'Is that all you can do?' roared Ragnar, laughing.

But Iorek was much cleverer than Ragnar. He wasn't really in trouble.

'I am the winner!' cried Ragnar to the Panserbjørne. He looked around at them. Then Iorek suddenly attacked him with his great strong body. He hit Ragnar as hard as he could – and killed him.

'Yes, that is all,' said Iorek. He turned to the Panserbjørne.

'Bears,' he cried, 'who is your king?'

'Iorek Byrnison!' they all shouted together.

CHAPTER 9
Another world

Lord Asriel was still a prisoner of the Ice Bears. He did not know that Ragnar was dead and Iorek Byrnison was now king. Lyra and Roger went to tell him. The bear outside the prison opened the heavy wood door. But inside it wasn't an ordinary prison. Asriel had a lot of rooms. They weren't cold and wet and dark. They were warm and comfortable. Inside the first room there were big expensive chairs and desks, and there was a big fire in the corner.

But Lord Asriel was not pleased to see Lyra.

'No! Get out!' he cried. 'I did not send for you!'

Then he saw Roger and he stopped shouting.

'This is Roger,' Lyra said to Asriel.

'Pleased to meet you, Roger,' said Asriel and then he called his man.

'Find Roger a bedroom,' he said. 'He looks tired. I'm sure he needs to sleep.'

Roger followed the man out of the room.

'Lyra, sit next to me for a moment,' said Asriel.

'I don't understand,' said Lyra. She looked around the comfortable rooms. 'You're a prisoner, aren't you?'

'Ragnar wanted me to study Dust,' he said. 'So he gave me these rooms and all the things I need. Dust joins people and their dæmons. When you cut the energy lines between a person and a dæmon, it makes a lot of energy.'

'But what is it?' asked Lyra.

'Dust? Well, I'm going to find out.'

He waited for a moment. Then he said, 'You have brought me the one thing I need. Now go and sleep.'

Asriel took Lyra to the bedroom where Roger was sleeping. Lyra couldn't stop thinking about everything, but she was very tired. Soon she fell asleep too.

Lyra woke up suddenly. Roger's bed was empty, and there was no sign of Lord Asriel. His things were not there now.

Lyra quickly took out her alethiometer. She could not believe what it told her.

She called Iorek, and climbed onto his back. Iorek ran across the ice. Soon they saw Lord Asriel and Roger.

'The alethiometer says he will do something bad to Roger,' Lyra told Iorek.

They got closer, but the ice became too thin for Iorek. He was too heavy and Lyra had to go on alone. She cried as she said goodbye to Iorek.

Then she carefully walked across the thin ice.

Lyra went over an icy hill and saw Lord Asriel. He had a strange machine and he was turning it on. Roger was joined to the machine, he couldn't escape. The machine started to glow with energy. Suddenly there was a loud sound and a strong white light, and the machine killed Roger's dæmon. Energy roared into the air. It cut open the sky – there was a door to other worlds.

Lyra ran towards Asriel's machine, but Roger wasn't there any more. Then she heard a voice across the icy land. Lyra turned around and saw Mrs Coulter. She was walking across the ice.

'What have you done?' Mrs Coulter asked Lord Asriel. She was looking up at the door in the sky.

Mrs Coulter came slowly closer to Asriel. Suddenly, he took her in his arms and they kissed. 'Will you come with me, Marisa?' he asked.

'I'm too frightened,' she answered. Asriel turned to Lyra.

'You wanted to see the North,' he said to her. 'You wanted to learn about Dust. Now you can.'

'Not with you!' cried Lyra. 'How could you do that to Roger!'

'You don't understand,' said Lord Asriel. 'This is much more important than one child.' Then he walked into the light and disappeared.

The ice around Mrs Coulter and Lyra was starting to break.

'Come with me, Lyra,' said Mrs Coulter.

'No,' answered Lyra. 'I don't want you for my mother.'

The ice broke into pieces. Mrs Coulter moved slowly away on one piece. Lyra looked at the alethiometer. There was glowing Dust all around it. Suddenly the hands started to go round fast.

'Pan!' said Lyra. 'Perhaps Dust isn't bad ... Perhaps Dust lives ... Perhaps it is good.' She looked at the alethiometer closely.

'It says that I know the way.' The door in the sky was getting bigger. Through the door, Lyra could see a big city.

'Come on, Pan,' she said. 'We'll follow the Dust. We'll learn about it, and we'll bring Roger back! We'll find him, and then we'll know what to do.'

Together, Lyra and Pan walked through the glowing door – and into a different world.

THE WRITER

**Philip Pullman is the writer of the trilogy, *His Dark Materials*.
The Golden Compass (or *Northern Lights*) is the first book in the trilogy.
Here, Philip Pullman talks about his life and his writing.**

Where and when did your life begin?
I was born in 1946 in Norfolk in the east of England. My family moved a lot - I went to school in Norfolk, Zimbabwe, Australia and finally north Wales! Then, I studied English at Oxford University.

You travelled a lot!
Yes, and in those days, people travelled by ship. It was a wonderful way to see the world.

When did you start writing?
When I was very young. I told stories to my friends and my younger brother. They weren't very good – but I didn't stop writing.

Did people around you want you to write?
No, they laughed at me, but that was good. It didn't stop me - I wanted to write even more.

Did you become a writer after university?
No, I was a teacher, but I always wrote in my own time. I became a full-time writer after *The Golden Compass* came out in 1995.

Where do you write?
I wrote *The Golden Compass* in the garden shed. But then my family and I moved house, and I gave the shed to a friend. So now I work in a big room inside my house.

Did you know …?

✦ Philip writes with a pen and paper, not on a computer.

✦ He found the name Serafina Pekkala in a Helsinki phone book.

✦ He kept a very large rat in his writing shed.

✦ You can read *His Dark Materials* in 39 different languages.

✦ You can read more about him on www.philip-pullman.com

Who is your favourite character in *The Golden Compass*?
I like writing about Mrs Coulter. She'll do anything to get what she wants. I wouldn't like to know her in real life.

Do you still travel a lot?
No, I've never been interested in travelling really. It's too uncomfortable and hot. I like staying at home.

What books did you read when you were young?
I liked books for adults and comics. I loved Superman and Batman.

Why do you write?
Three reasons. One, money. If I don't write well, I can't pay the bills. Two, I want people to remember me for something. Three, I love making things, including stories.

What do you think of the film *The Golden Compass*?
I'm very happy with it!

Who is your favourite character in *The Golden Compass*? Which is your favourite dæmon?

What do these words mean? You can use a dictionary.
trilogy adult shed character full-time rat

LYRA'S WORLD

"Lyra's world is like our world in some ways, but it's also very different."

OXFORD

As in our world, Lyra's Oxford is a centre of learning. The streets of Oxford are quiet. There are no cars. People travel by riverboat, by airship, and by carriage.

◎ Golden Compass Fact: Jordan College is the richest and most beautiful of all colleges in Oxford.

SVALBARD

Svalbard is an icy land in the far north. It is the home of the Panserbjørne, the armoured Ice Bears.

◎ Golden Compass Fact: The join between Lyra's world and other worlds is very thin in Svalbard. Lord Asriel goes there to find a way through.

SKY FERRIES AND AIRSHIPS

Sky ferries are a very comfortable way to travel. They can carry many people. Lee Scoresby has an airship.

◎ Golden Compass Fact: Sky ferries and other machines use a strange, glowing form of energy called 'anbaric' power.

LONDON

Lyra's London is a very big city. It has many fine buildings and important offices; for example, the Magisterium. Mrs Coulter lives there.

◎ Golden Compass Fact: People travel around the busy streets by 'anbaric' carriage.

You can make one of these changes to your world:
✦ no cars ✦ travel by carriage ✦ dæmons ✦ a doorway to another world
Which will you choose?

THE WITCHES OF ENARA

The witches of Enara live in the forests of the north. They are good fighters. They can fly and travel a long way from their dæmons. People cannot do this. Their queen, Serafina Pekkala, is 300 years old.

◉ Golden Compass Fact:
50 years ago the Gyptian Farder Coram and Serafina fell in love when he saved her. They cannot be together because witches live for hundreds of years. Now Farder Coram is old, but she is still young and beautiful.

THE PANSERBJØRNE

The Ice Bears live at the top of the world, in the coldest place. They prefer to live away from people, but they are very loyal. Bears do not have dæmons, but a Panserbjørne is nothing without its armour.

◉ Golden Compass Fact:
They make their own armour from sky-iron. They collect it from falling stars that land in Svalbard.

THE GYPTIANS

There are six Gyptian tribes with many families in each tribe. Ma Costa is head of the Costa family. They often come to Oxford to trade. Billy Costa meets Lyra there. The Gyptian King is John Faa. Farder Coram is a clever, older Gyptian. He gives advice to John Faa.

◉ Golden Compass Fact:
Their dæmons are usually birds or cats.

Which of the three groups above would you like to join? Why?

What do these words mean? You can use a dictionary.

carriage   forest   advice   tribe   trade   iron   loyal

FIND YOUR DÆMON

In the world of *The Golden Compass*, everyone has a dæmon. Your dæmon is part of you, but it lives outside your body. It takes the form of a talking animal. If you are quick and clever, you could have a cat, for example. What's your dæmon?

1 Which of these is most like you?

a You think quickly; you always do what you want.
b You love being at home; you take life easy.
c You are clever; you spend a lot of time alone.
d You are quiet; you think about other people.

2 How many close friends do you have?

a Two or three really close friends.
b Lots of friends, but they're not very close.
c One best friend.
d A large group of good friends.

3 How do you feel when you walk into a party?

a Relaxed. I love parties.
b A bit worried if I don't know anyone.
c Fine. I'm sure someone will talk to me.
d I never go to parties.

4 How important is doing well at school to you?

a Quite important. I really try hard!
b Not at all. I want an easy life.
c Very. I want to be the best at everything.
d Not very. It's more important to be happy.

What do these words mean? You can use a dictionary.
relaxed forest rude snake spirit squirrel wild

5 How hard-working are you?

a Quite. Sometimes I'm lazy.
b When I have work to do, I do it.
c I hate sitting around doing nothing.
d I'm usually doing something.

6 What do other people think of you?

a A bit wild, but a really nice person.
b Open and friendly.
c Sometimes they think I'm rude.
d Hard to talk to at first.

7 If someone pushes in front of you, what do you do?

a I ask them to move.
b I'm not happy, but I don't say anything.
c It doesn't worry me.
d I say something loud to my friends.

8 Which of these is your favourite?

a A forest.
b Open country.
c Mountains.
d The sea.

◆ ★ ◆ ★ ◆ ★ ◆ ★ ◆ ★ ◆ ★ ◆ ★ ◆ ★ ◆ ★ ◆ ★ ◆ ★ ◆ ★

How many a, b, c and d answers have you got? Add up your score and look at the key.

Mostly a

Your dæmon will be quick-thinking, but sometimes it won't do what you ask. You have a wild side, but your dæmon will show your softer side. Your dæmon will be fast, beautiful and clever. How about a wild cat?
Who's in this group? Lyra and Pan

Mostly b

You love home and your dæmon will too. It will be like a pet, perhaps a cat or dog. If you love to be outside, perhaps your dæmon is a squirrel. You probably won't be a Jordan scholar or a great traveller but your dæmon will be hard-working and full of energy.
Who's in this group? Roger and Salcilia

Mostly c

Your dæmon will be unusual and dangerous. Perhaps it is a snake? People say bad things about snakes, but you can work hard on your good points. You have a cool head and you can look after yourself. There are some very fine dæmons in this group, but they like playing tricks.
Who's in this group? Mrs Coulter and the Golden Monkey

Mostly d

Most people in this group have a bird dæmon. You have a free spirit and you are always on the move. If you love animals and plants, perhaps your dæmon is a river bird. You like being in a group, but you prefer to choose the group yourself. You like living wild and follow your own road through life.
Who's in this group? Serafina Pekkala and Kaisa; Lee Scoresby and Hester; the Gyptians and their birds

53

CHAPTERS 1–3

Before you read

You can use your dictionary.

1   Put these words in the right sentences.

machines   prison   compass   bear   energy   prophecy   ice   dust

a)   A ... tells you which way to go.

b)   If you do not clean your house, there will be a lot of ... .

c)   Many people have ... to wash their clothes and plates.

d)   You put ... in drinks to make them cold.

e)   A ... tells you something about the future.

f)   The police took the man to ... .

g)   We need ... for heat and light.

h)   My favourite animal is a ... .

2   Look at 'People and daemons' on pages 4–5. Answer the questions.

a)   Who is good, do you think? Who is bad?

b)   How does Lyra meet all these people, do you think?

After you read

3   Are these sentences true or false? Correct the false sentences.

a)   Fra Pavel and the Magisterium like Lord Asriel and his ideas.

b)   Lord Asriel wants to find out where Dust comes from.

c)   The Gobblers take Roger and Salcilia from the college gardens.

d)   Lyra and Pan really want to go to London with Mrs Coulter.

e)   The Master doesn't want Mrs Coulter to know about the alethiometer.

4   **Answer the questions.**

a)   Why does Fra Pavel take the Master to prison?

b)   Why does Lyra like London at first?

c)   How does Lyra keep the alethiometer safe?

d)   How does Lyra feel when the Golden Monkey pulls Pan away from her?

e)   What do Lyra and Pan learn in Mrs Coulter's study?

f)   Why does Pan change into a bird?

5   **What do you think?**

a)   Why does Mrs Coulter take Lyra to London?

b)   Why does Lyra have to keep the alethiometer a secret?

CHAPTERS 4-6

Before you read

6   Match the two parts of the sentences.
   a) Bears make their own ...   i)   is a dangerous job.
   b) Being a spy ...   ii) helps you find things out.
   c) A bear roars ...   iii) armour.
   d) Doing an experiment ...   iv) the Gyptians.
   e) I'm going to cut ...   v)   is a way of travelling.
   f) The Tartars attacked ...   vi) the cake into eight pieces.
   g) An airship ...   vii) when it is angry.

7   Lyra and Pan are alone in London. They don't know London very
   well. The Gobblers will be after them and the Master is in prison.
   What will they do, do you think?

After you read

8   Match the two parts of the sentences.
   a) John Faa   i) tells the Gyptians to go to Bolvangar.
   b) Ma Costa   ii) tries to use the alethiometer, but can't.
   c) Mrs Coulter's Spy-flies   iii) is taking the Gyptians to rescue the children.
   d) Farder Coram   iv) takes Lyra to meet the King of the Gyptians.
   e) Serafina Pekkala   v) are looking for Lyra.

9   Complete the sentences with the correct name.
   Roger   Lyra   John Faa   Experimental Station   Lee Scoresby
   Iorek Byrnison   Hester
   a) The Noorderlicht is a ship that belongs to ... .
   b) ... travels by airship.
   c) ... is Lee Scoresby's daemon.
   d) The armour in the Magisterium office in Trollesund belongs to ... .
   e) The Samoyeds take ... from the Gyptians. They go to the ... .
   f) Lyra finds ... at the Station.

10 What do these people say, do you think?
   a) Mrs Coulter, when she learns that the Gyptians have rescued Lyra.
   b) Lyra, when she hears that the Gobblers have taken Billy Costa.
   c) Iorek, when he sees his armour again.
   d) Ma Costa, when she sees Billy.
   e) John Faa, when they find the Samoyeds have taken Lyra.

CHAPTERS 7–9

Before you read

11 Choose the correct word.

    a) In a war / palace people fight and kill each other.

    b) The king lives in a war / palace.

12 What do you think?

    a) How is Lyra going to find out where the Gyptians are?

    b) The next chapter is 'A dangerous machine'. Why is the machine dangerous, do you think?

    c) Will Lyra and Roger escape from the Experimental Station?

After you read

13 Put these sentences in order.

    a) Serafina tells Lee of a prophecy about Lyra and a war.

    b) The Ice Bears take Lyra and Pan prisoner and take them to King Ragnar Sturlusson.

    c) Mrs Coulter saves Lyra and Pan from the cutting machine.

    d) Lyra learns who her real parents are.

    e) Lyra tricks Ragnar Sturlusson into a fight with Iorek.

    f) Lyra breaks the cutting machine.

    g) The witches and the Gyptians attack the Tartars and save the children.

    h) Lyra and the other children escape from the Experimental Station.

    i) Lyra falls out of Lee Scoresby's airship.

14 Choose the correct answer.

    a) Lord Asriel is working hard / dying in prison.

    b) He is / isn't pleased when he sees Roger.

    c) He has / hasn't found out what Dust is.

    d) He takes Lyra / Roger and leaves Lyra / Roger behind.

    e) When Lord Asriel's machine kills Roger's dæmon, a door / window opens into another world.

    f) Lord Asriel cares / doesn't care about Roger.

    g) Mrs Coulter follows / doesn't follow them into the new world.

15 What do you think?

    a) Will Lyra and Pan find Roger?

    b) What will happen when they go into the other world?